We constantly travel the globe to discover new gemstones.
Scan this QR code on a mobile device to read the latest news.

D0892356

The Little Book of Gemstones (A)
www.tggc.com

All enquiries should be directed to:
The Genuine Gemstone Company Limited, Unit 2D
Eagle Road, Moons Moat
Redditch, Worcestershire, B98 9HF

ISBN: 978-0-9559972-3-5
Published by The Genuine Gemstone Company Limited
Designed by The Genuine Gemstone Company Limited

THE LITTLE **BOOK OF GEMSTONES**

A

By Steve Bennett

INTRODUCTION

Welcome to the world of Mother Nature's treasures:
a world full of colourful locations, colourful people,
colourful stories and, of course - colourful gems.

This series has been written in an A to Z
encyclopaedic format, so that you can dip in and out
at your leisure. Whenever you come across a new
gemstone or hear someone mention a jewellery term
that you have not heard before, you can easily use
these books to quickly find out more.

Steve Bennett

BIJOUX DE MER

Abalone A gemstone created in the sea, with a fusion of blues and greens. Just like the ocean's waves with swirling and rolling in beautiful patterns.

Considered a delicacy by many throughout the world, the Abalone, or Ear Shell, is a Gastropod: a member of the Mollusc family of sea creatures. The creature has a univalve shell, similar to the Limpet and attaches itself to rocks or structures under the sea by suction.

The shell of the Abalone is used in jewellery, and the exceptional and mesmerising colours of the shell are a by-product from farming the shellfish for its meat, making the crafting of jewellery from the Gastropod very eco-friendly.

From one side the shell looks rather dull and unexciting and is quite often covered by other sea crustaceans; but from the other side it shines with an array of stunning colours and beautiful iridescence, displaying vivid blues, greens and pinks, all combined in a spectacular modern art styled pattern.

Each shell embodies a unique display of colour and markings, almost like the human fingerprint, therefore no two pieces are exactly the same. The gem is ideal for use in many large jewellery designs, from pendants and big, dangly earrings, to bracelets and Sterling Silver rings. In addition to jewellery, you may have seen this gem inlayed into acoustic guitars.

In New Zealand the Maori name for the Abalone Shell is the Paua Shell (pronounced Par-war). Therefore when you see the name 'Paua', this refers to Abalone Shell that is only from New Zealand. The best comparison would be Zultanite and Diaspore: Zultanite is Diaspore, but only when it is found in Turkey.

Around its coast line there are both commercial organisations and hobbyists extracting the gem from the sea bed.

Once on dry land, each shell is hand cut, buffed and polished by experts who understand the natural curves and patterns of the shell, ensuring each piece takes full advantage of all the colours of the ocean. I am not sure whether it is due to the shell's array of wonderful colours, or the fact that their next door neighbours often boast about their prized Opals, that many in New Zealand refer to the Paua as 'the opal of the sea'. Without doubt the Paua ranks amongst the finest Abalone on the planet, displaying the most intense blues and greens – which many locals

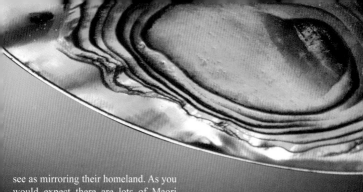

see as mirroring their homeland. As you would expect there are lots of Maori legend and folklore surrounding their local treasure.

Adamantine When light is reflected off the surface of a gemstone it is referred to as "lustre" (also spelt "luster").

Several transparent gemstones with a high refractive index are said to possess an adamantine lustre. The word is derived from "Adamas", the Ancient Greek word for Diamond; a gemstone which displays a dazzling adamantine lustre.

Technically speaking, only those gemstones with a high refractive index tend to have an adamantine lustre. If you have invested in a portable refractometer you will be aware that the reading stops at around 1.85, therefore if you don't get a reading whilst analysing a gemstone, and if it also has a fantastic lustre, then you have already started to dramatically narrow the range of possible gems that it might be.

Other gemstones that feature this captivating lustre include Zircon and Demantoid Garnet.

Gemstones with a high refractive index, but not quite that of Diamond, Zircon or Demantoid, are said to have a subadamantine lustre. These include some members of the Garnet family and fine examples of Sapphire.

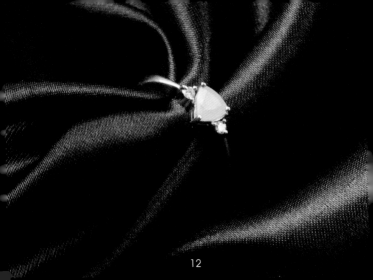

Adamite Possibly the rarest gemstone we have ever sold at Gems TV.

First discovered in 1866, Adamite is named after French mineralogist Gilbert-Joseph Adam who first documented the mineral.

Rarely set into jewellery, Adamite is a real favourite amongst gem and mineral collectors as it fluoresces a bright green colour under UV light.

Crystal Healers are also very fond of Adamite and claim that the mineral helps one to properly communicate emotions, thus increasing our levels of creativity.

In addition it is said to have a positive effect on the heart, lungs and throat.

However, if you own a piece of Adamite or are one of the handful of people across the globe that have ever been fortunate enough to purchase a gem-quality piece made into jewellery, my advice is that whilst it might possess crystal healing benefits, if you touch the gemstone, you should wash your hands afterwards as the mineral has the presence of arsenic.

Adamite grows into wedge shaped crystals that are usually yellow-green in colour, but it is also found in blue or violet colours.

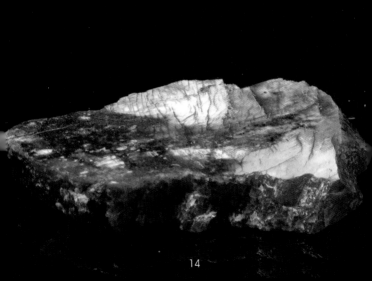

14

Adularescence is a vibrant, natural optical effect similar to the shimmering appearance of the moon on a cloudless evening. Its name is derived from "adularia", a mineralogist term for Moonstone.

When a gem displays an attractive light, which appears to float below its surface, the effect is known as adularescence. Caused by the physical crystal structure in certain gemstones, it can be seen near the surface of several gems where a ghost-like reflection with a bluish-whitish colour is visible. To maximise this glorious visual effect, these gems are often cabochon cut.

This shimmering effect is visible only in certain gemstones that have a layered type structure. These layers alternate in thickness; the thinner ones are so small that the eye cannot detect the visible wavelengths, scattering the light in multiple directions.

When adularescence is witnessed in Labradorite it is often referred to as labradorescence. In Opals it is known as opalescence, but be careful not to confuse this with 'play of colour', which is a different optical phenomena. Although the effect is most noticeable in Moonstones, Labradorite and Opals, you can occasionally see it in Rose Quartz and some Brazilian Agates.

In Southern Brazil we unearthed some very unusual Lavender Quartz and every single piece demonstrated wonderful adularescence.

Afghanistan Positioned at the crossroads of ancient Indian, Persian, European and Asian civilizations, Afghanistan has been at the heart of gem trading routes and expeditions for thousands of years, which have included such eminent figures as Alexander the Great, Marco Polo and the Moguls.

Unfortunately, today Afghanistan is a country known more for its conflicts. But below ground, gemstone mining is still happening and a kaleidoscope of popular gemstones are being unearthed.

17

Female lapidarist cutting gems in Ishkashim.

Ruby from Murgab; Spinel from the Kuh-i- Lal mine; Turquoise from Eastern Tajikistan, plus Emerald, Red Jasper, Tourmaline, Amazonite, Kyanite and Garnets: all of these combine to make Afghanistan one of the most prolific countries in the world for gemmologists.

It is said that the famous "Black Prince's Ruby" in the Crown Jewels, which is really a Spinel, originated from the Kuh- i-Lal mine in Afghanistan. Writings by Marco Polo suggest that the mine is one of the oldest gem mines in the world still in operation and records trace its existence back to 101AD. This mine yields not only Spinel, but also Rubies and Garnets. As all three can be similar in colour it is understandable that in years gone by the three gems would often be mistaken by gem explorers, who did not have the scientific tools available to us today.

The mine is a maze of over 400 tunnels, and today's miners occasionally come across ancient bones of miners who were trapped in collapsed mine shafts.

If the fact that Spinel mining took place in 101AD impresses you, then how about the fact that Afghans have been mining for Lapis Lazuli for over 6500 years in the Badakhshan province and Panjshir valley! It has been said by many gemmologists that Afghanistan has both the largest and best supply of this gemstone in the world.

The landscape of the area is stunning, with the skyline being dominated by the impressive Hindu Kush mountain range which rises to over six thousand metres above sea level (19500 feet). Like most gem mining in Afghanistan, the area is incredibly difficult to access and if you were to follow the mountain to the East you soon arrive at the heart of the Himalayas and travel across Northern Pakistan and India. As I mentioned in the introduction to this book, gem mining often takes place in the most inhospitable areas and the

Panjshir valley is a case in point with its long, freezing cold winters followed by dry, boiling hot summers.

Although it is famous for its Lapis Lazuli, more recently there have also been small discoveries of Emeralds, Tourmaline, Kunzite, Ruby, Aquamarine and Yellow Beryl in the valley. In some sense it is not surprising that this area is rich in gemstones, when you consider the huge geological event that was needed to create the Himalayas. The mountain range was formed as the result of the collision of the Indo- Pakistan and Asian crustal plates.

My gem hunting friend Andy, who works for the GIA and who kindly took these photos for me in Afghanistan, explains that the Emerald Mines are some of the most difficult of all to reach.

Once you pass several thousand metres the slopes become too steep for the donkeys and the mules to ascend, so the last two hours of the hike up to the Emerald Mine must be done on foot. The air is so thin at this extreme altitude that even for the locals progress is very slow.

Although the area is difficult to reach, I have been told that at its peak there are over a thousand artisanal miners searching for their personal fortune in the area, with over 100 of them working at a small deposit known locally as the Buzmal Mine. Despite the harsh conditions, I have heard that some miners brave the conditions to work virtually the entire year round.

Most Emerald mining in Afghanistan today is run by small family businesses in the Panjshir Valley. These tiny mining operations are located some 3,000 to 4,000 metres above sea level and are extremely difficult to reach. Afghan Emeralds are often more transparent and somewhat brighter than those found in the likes of Colombia and Siberia.

The Jegdalek mines, located only 40 miles to the East of Kabul, produce some fine quality Rubies and Sapphires. Although the distance is not great, my gem hunter in Afghanistan tells me, "the first part of the journey is on a fairly major road, however, due to the recent wars there are many land mines and the route is very treacherous. As you get closer to the mines the road turns to a dirt track and eventually you have to drive along a shallow stream bed." The Jegdalek mines are unusual in that the gems are being mined in a geological belt made up primarily of marble. In some places the marble is up to 900 feet deep. Here there are some 400 mines all being operated by artisanal miners, who in the main only use a hammer and a pick axe. Many of them make shelters out of the rocks they excavate and then once inside chip away at the marble to remove their treasure.

To the North of the Jegdalek Ruby and Sapphire mines are the Kunzite mines in the Mawi Valley which is located in the Kolum district. Here some of the finest quality material in the world is discovered. The Mawi Valley Kunzites are truly gorgeous and emit wonderful phosphorescence. The Kunzite here tends to grow in large pegmatites and in the middle of the summer up to 500 miners arrive trying to uncover this beautiful and valuable pink Spodumene. Even in the extremely harsh winter my Afghan Gem Hunter, Zeeshan Khan, tells me that a dedicated few still somehow manage to continue mining. To arrive at the area where the gemstones are most likely to occur, miners have to remove around 10 to 20 metres of clay. As with other remote mining areas, the tools they have at their disposal are very primitive indeed.

Throughout history, all of these different mining locations, with their treasure trove of different gemstones, are believed to have helped locals trade their findings for weapons, in order to defend themselves. The country has had so many different conflicts: the Greeks invaded in 327BC, Mongols in 1227, the British from 1838 - 1919, the Russians from 1979 to 1988. All of these wars motivated indigenous tribes people to explore for new gem deposits in order to protect their families.

Various gemstones from Badakhshan.

23

Agate This gemstone has been prized since antiquity and is a variety of Chalcedony, which in turn is a member of the Quartz family.

It was given its name by Theophrastus, a Greek philosopher who is believed to have discovered the gem on the banks of the river Achates in the 4th century BC. The gemstone was later mentioned in the Bible as one of the "stones of fire".

Made from silicon dioxide, it has a glassy (vitreous) lustre, and registers 7 in hardness on the Mohs scale. Being such a hard stone, Agate is often used to make brooches and pins. Additionally, as it can also resist acids (unlike a lot of other gemstones) it has been used to make mortars and pestles to press and combine chemicals.

Many Agates originate in cavities of molten rock, where gas bubbles trapped in solidifying lava are replaced with alkali and silica bearing solutions. Formed as a banded round nodule (similar to the rings of a tree trunk). The gem boasts an exquisite assortment of shapes and colours of bands, which may be seen clearly if a lapidarist cuts the sections at a right angle to the layers: this is sometimes referred to as Riband Agate. Other types of Agate include Onyx (Onyx is almost always a dyed Agate), Sardonyx, Ring Agate (encompassing bands of different colours), Moss Agate (with green banding), Blue Lace Agate, Turritella Agate, Snake Skin Agate, Rainbow Agate and Fire Agate.

Myths and legends suggest that when a person wears Agate, they become more pleasant and agreeable. It is believed to quench thirst, protect against viruses (including fever) and to cure insomnia. Some tribes in Brazil also believe that Agate can even cure the stings of scorpions and bites from poisonous snakes. Cut off from society often without modern medicines Agate is used for a variety of ailments.

26

Alexandrite is a very valuable and rare Colour Change Chrysoberyl. It is highly regarded by gem experts, enthusiasts and connoisseurs alike.

The gem's uniqueness and value is not often apparent at first sight, but finely faceted, one carat pieces or more rank amongst the most expensive gems in the world – far rarer than even fine Diamonds, Rubies, Emeralds and Sapphires.

It is said that Alexandrite was discovered near the Tokovaya River in the Ural Mountains of Russia, on the same day that Alexander II (1818-1881) came of age. Hence the gemstone was named after the 16 year old future Tsar. This was deemed appropriate not just because it was discovered on Russian soil, but also because its extraordinary ability to change colour from red to green echoed the colours of the Russian flag at that time.

The first person to raise its awareness in public, Count Lev Alekseevich Perovskii (1792-1856), believed the stone to be a variety of Emerald, but noting it had a strange mineral content, passed it for a second opinion to the Finnish mineralogist, Nils Gustaf Nordenskiold.

When initially studying the gem, Nordenskiold was also of the opinion that it was a type of Emerald, but as he was confused by its greater hardness he continued to review it. One evening when working by candle light, he was surprised to see the gem was no longer green but had turned a raspberry red. He then declared the gemstone a new form of Chrysoberyl, which would later be given its own distinct name. Today we know that Alexandrite is in fact a colour change variety of Chrysoberyl.

But now for some bad news! It is a misconception that gemstones that are named "colour change" gemstones physically change colour. The reality is that when viewed under different lighting conditions, the gem only appears to change colour. When you buy a "colour change" gemstone, to view the strongest change you need to view the gem under candescent lighting (direct sunlight), which has high proportions of blue and green light, and then immediately view it under incandescent lighting (for example a light bulb), which has a higher balance of red light. Therefore, when you view Alexandrite in daylight the gem appears green, but when the light source is reddish (incandescent), the gem shows hues of purple or red. Effectively you are looking at an optical illusion! Most changes are incredibly subtle, so the saying that Alexandrite looks like Emerald by day and Ruby by night, is a little bit of an exaggeration. That said, Alexandrite is a real treasure: so incredibly rare that few jewellers have ever even held a piece!

Not only does Alexandrite have the ability to change colour, it is also a pleochroic gemstone; this means different colours can be seen when the gem is viewed from different angles. The gem is also very durable, measuring 8.5 on the Mohs scale, making it ideal for setting into all types of precious jewellery.

It is also one of three birthstones for the month of June (Pearl and Moonstone being the other two). In times of upset Alexandrite is believed to strengthen the wearer's intuition, and thus helps find new ways forward where logic and practical thinking will not provide an answer; it is also known to aid creativity and inspire one's imagination.

Although Alexandrite was originally discovered in Russia, other mines of this treasured gem have since been discovered in Brazil and Zimbabwe. More importantly, finds in Sri Lanka and India are providing great interest for those in the gem industry, as they are believed to be part of the same vein running down vertically from the original source in the Ural Mountains. However, many gemmologists still believe a fine example known undisputedly to have come from Russia is a real rarity with enormous value.

The number one criterion in valuing Alexandrite for me is the amount of colour change, combined with its clarity and then its size. I would happily pay more for a half carat piece which demonstrated an obvious colour shift, than a one carat piece where you had to use your vivid imagination to see any difference. Generally speaking cloudy Alexandrites have more chance of a stronger colour change than clear ones,

but if you can find one that has a clean crystal structure and a vivid colour change then you are indeed looking at a very rare gem.

32

Allochromatic gems are those which receive their colour from the presence of impurities.

The array of beautiful colours we see in natural gemstones can be created by one of three events:

Firstly, it can be due to the inherent chemical makeup of the crystal; these gems are known as idiochromatic. Peridot for example is idiochromatic.

Secondly, a gem's colour can be caused by the optical properties of the gem and its reflection from or just under its surface.

Thirdly, and most common, gems coloured by the presence of impurities are known as allochromatic. All allochromatic gemstones would be colourless without the presence of impurities. The main elements that add colour to gemstones are titanium, chromium, manganese, iron, cobalt, nickel, and copper. The presence of these elements in gems such as Sapphire, Beryl, Spinel and Quartz are the sources of their vibrant array of beautiful colours.

Take Corundum as an example. In its purest form it is colourless (White Sapphire). When traces of iron are present we see a gorgeous Yellow Sapphire, add a small amount of titanium alongside the iron and you have the famous Blue Sapphire and when chromium is added to Corundum it becomes a rich red Ruby.

Without the presence of impurities, transparent allochromatic gems are colourless and opaque gems are white. In the case of Quartz and Beryl, the colourless varieties are more common, thus actually making them less valuable than those with impurities. For example, compare the price of a colourless 2 carat Beryl (known as Goshenite), to an equivalent carat weight of light blue Beryl (Aquamarine), and the price increases substantially. Then take the colourless Beryl, add a trace of chromium or vanadium and the price explodes exponentially as the gem now becomes an Emerald.

However, other gems such as Tourmaline and Jade are rarely found colourless making them more valuable than their coloured equivalents. The allochromatic gemstone Spinel, available in almost every colour imaginable, has yet to be discovered colourless.

35

Allotropic

How can graphite and Diamonds both be pure carbon?

First let's start by explaining what the word means. Allotropic chemical elements are those that can take on different forms. The word allotropy is derived from the Greek "allos", meaning "other", and "tropos", meaning "manner".

Now compare the soft graphite in a pencil to the hardest mineral on the planet - Diamond. Both are in fact made of the same material, carbon. But if they are the same, how is it that one is super soft, while the other is incredibly hard?

Graphite is formed at low temperatures and under little pressure very near to the Earth's surface. As it forms, its layers are not bonded together very well, making it soft, and ideal for use in pencils and lubricants. Diamonds on the other hand are believed to be created some 93 miles below the Earth's surface, in extreme heat and under immense pressure. This tough environment compresses the carbon atoms into a compact and extremely strong crystal structure.

All these forces are applied for millions of years, and combine to create beautiful, hardwearing Diamonds.

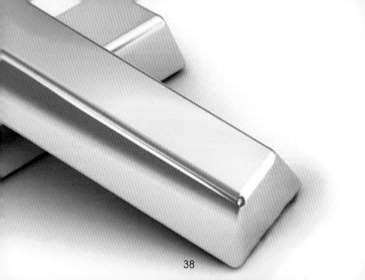

Alloys An alloy is a metal that has been made from two or more different metals. In jewellery terms, most gold and silver pieces are not 100% pure and are made into an alloy to improve their strength.

Gold is such a soft metal that even biting it, you would leave a large imprint of your teeth. Therefore without being merged with stronger metals, gold would be pretty useless in jewellery for everyday wear.

The percentage of gold in the alloyed metal is known as its fineness and in the UK the hallmark applied by the Assay office details how much gold is present in the final blend. Not only by creating alloys can we make Gold and Silver stronger, we can actually change their colour. For example by adding Silver and other white metals to Gold (pure Gold is always yellow in colour), we are able to produce White Gold. By adding a percentage of copper to gold when creating an alloy, Rose Gold can be created.

Pewter used to be annealed with lead to make it more workable for the Pewterer. However, when it was later discovered that lead could be dangerous, the metal pretty much vanished. Only very recently has a new alloy been created where just two percent of a stronger metal being added has made the metal once again suitable.

Alluvial Deposits Derived from the Latin word "alluere", "to wash against", alluvial deposits are often a combination of soils, sediments, stones and minerals that have come to rest in historic river beds.

The amount of solid matter carried by a large river can be enormous: the Amazon River is reported to relocate over 700 million tonnes of sediment and rocks to the sea every year!

When exposed rocks at the surface of the Earth weather over a period of time, gems may be released. Some of these rocks will dissolve completely,

while others will be broken down into smaller pieces. The smaller, loose rocks that survive the erosion process are often washed into rivers or streams and as gems are heavier than most other materials they can easily be trapped in depressions in stream or river beds; this is how concentrations of gems are found.

Over millions of years these rivers dry up and alluvial deposits can be found many hundreds of miles from the nearest river or sea. Gems that are mined from alluvial deposits tend to be rounded, due to the fact they have been rolling along river or sea beds.

Gem traders in Ilakaka sorting gems form the local alluvial deposit.

As landscapes continue to change over millions of years, many alluvial deposits end up being buried deep underground. What I find most interesting about alluvial deposit mining, is that of the dozens of mines of this type I have visited around the world, no two have used the same method to search and extract the rough material. Whilst small, independent artisanal miners may dig deep shafts and then have their neighbouring miner lower them down their hole, big corporate companies will use heavy plant machinery.

When an alluvial deposit is mined, it can often yield a wide variety of different gemstones. Madagascar, which currently has many alluvial mining activities, boasts one of the widest arrays of beautiful coloured gemstones in the world.

Searching for Morganite in Madagascar. The deposit is some 30 metres down this shaft.

43

Almandine Garnet One of the oldest Garnets recorded by man, this beautiful gem was featured in writings by the Roman historian Pliny the Elder.

Varying in colour from a red to reddish orange through to a delicious, purplish red, Almandine is typically dark in tone. For thousands of years, Almandine Garnet has been mined in several locations around the world and is often given a different name based on where it is found.

The name is said to have been derived from the writing of Pliny the Elder who wrote of a stone coming from an Asian town called Alabanda. Often you will read Almandine Garnet incorrectly spelt as Almandite.

In Sri Lanka it has been called Ceylon Ruby and in days gone by when it was discovered in the Northern territories of Australia it was often referred to as Australian Ruby. Another popular member of the Garnet family, Mozambique Garnet, is in fact a mixture of Pyrope and Almandine Garnet.

Almandine is one of the more frequently discovered Garnets and today the gem is mined in Norway, Pakistan, India and America.

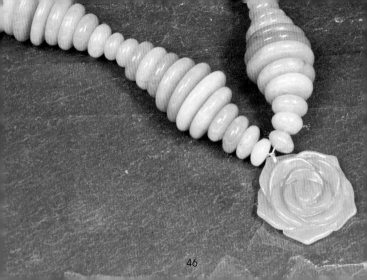

Amazonite This gem is named after the Amazon River; However, it has never been discovered near the river and we are yet to find a reliable source that can explain how the gem's name was derived.

Amazonite is a bluish green variety of microcline Feldspar and its appearance always resembles a piece of mottled modern art. This irregular hue varies from green to yellowish green to bluish green, with some specimens featuring white streaks.

Amazonite is not heat treated by man, so its colours are always natural. Those who specialise in this gemstone say its beauty comes to life when viewed at sunrise or sunset.

Its colour was always believed to have come from the presence of copper, as its colour is similar to that of other gems that include copper, however more recently it has been discovered that the colouring agent in Amazonite is actually lead. In the past, finer green Amazonite specimens have been mistaken for Jade. Amazonite has been said to help calm one's emotions and soothe nerves. It is also believed to enhance the ability to express oneself, but its strongest power of all is to make married life happier!

Amber is one of a few gems that is organic and is created from fossilised resin of ancient trees.

Over a period of millions of years and exposure to high temperature and pressure, the compressed resin eventually becomes Amber. Because it floats on salt water, if you take a stroll along the beaches on the East Coast of the UK, there is a small chance that you may discover your own piece of the precious stone washed up on the shore!

Interestingly enough, until the mid 19th century this was how most Amber was found, and back then it was appropriately named 'Seastone'. Amber's resin traps all kind of materials, and it is these inclusions which make every piece of Amber unique. The range of inclusions varies from frogs to bugs to leaves; it is not unusual to find a completely preserved fly or insect hidden inside the gem. The wealth of tiny insects trapped inside is due to the fact that when the resin leaked from the tree, it was incredibly sticky as its job was to stop insects from boring into the bark. 'Jurassic Park' may have given us an insight into how the world was a long time ago, but for Zoologists and Geologists, Amber is a lot more resourceful and to-date they have identified over one thousand

different species of extinct insects purely by studying the gemstone! It really is a most unique gem, providing a visual snapshot of what life was like around 50 million years ago.

The gem can be warm to touch and can create static electricity when rubbed. In years gone by its ability to create static was believed by many to be a magical power. In fact the word "electricity" originates from the Greek word for Amber, "electron". Many people believe that Amber brings good luck and aids well being.

The Baltic States of Estonia, Latvia and Lithuania provide much of the Amber set in jewellery today, as well as the popular Caribbean holiday destination, the Dominican Republic. Although predominately a rich orange colour, Amber can also be found in yellow, honey, brown and green (Green Amber is formed when plantation is trapped within the resin).

Although Amber is most commonly found in the Baltics, it has also been discovered in several other locations around the globe. In keeping with other naming conventions for Amber, where

Rumanite is named after its origin of Romania, Simetite which is Sicilian in origin; Burmite is the name given to Amber which is found in Burma.

Even though it is popular with local people, Burmite is often cloudy and therefore hides many of its hidden treasures locked within the gem. Therefore it is normally cheaper than those specimens found in Poland and the Baltics. That said, as many people who collect gemstones and jewellery often like to collect these items based on their origin, at Gems TV we source gems from a wide variety of countries.

Amblygonite is without doubt one of the unsung heroes of the gem world.

Although many believe this sensational gem was first discovered in the UK, Amblygonite was in fact initially discovered in the early 1800s in Germany, by Johann Breithaupt, a mineralogist who was credited with the discovery and identification of 47 different minerals!

I have a real soft spot for Amblyonite: its beauty is mesmerising and whenever I show a piece to someone in my office, the gem never fails to both stir emotions and to impress my guests. The gem's appearance often resembles a cross between Aquamarine and Paraiba Tourmaline. Its colour is tranquil when indoors, however when worn outdoors its appearance is as lively and sparkly as the sun dancing on the surface off the Mediterranean Sea on a summer afternoon. Unfortunately even though Amblygonite is a relatively common phosphate mineral, the supply of gem-quality pieces is very erratic and over the years I have only ever seen a few parcels of the gem being sold in the trade. If Amblygonite was not so scarce, I believe it would be one of the most highly regarded gemstones on the planet. For now it remains a specialist gemstone that aficionados and connoisseurs fight over whenever a piece is made available for sale.

Its name is derived from the Greek words for 'blunt' (amblus) and 'angle' (gouia), probably due to the unusual angles of the gem's cleavage. It is sometimes referred to as the 'Prophet Stone'.

Amblygonite is most often found in white and pastel shades of green, lilac, pink, and yellow, but rarely is of a transparent gem-quality material.

As the gem is rich in the chemical element lithium, it is often discovered in the same location as Tourmaline and Apatite.

The two largest gem-quality finds of Amblygonite have been in California and France. The current collection on sale at Gems TV was discovered in East Brazil where the Lavra mine, situated at Rio Jequitinhonha (half way between Minas Gerais and the coast), is famous for one of the largest Alexandrite finds in the world. On discovering possibly the most gorgeous Amblygonite ever unearthed, the mine owners partied hard for many days, saying that the occasion was as important as the time when Alexandrite was found. However, their initial excitement did not last long, as very little of the gem has yet been recovered.

Unfortunately, Amblygonite is very difficult to find. It is also a complete nightmare to cut! With four different directions of cleavage, even the very best lapidarists find the gem a real challenge to facet! When the clarity of the gem is of a high standard and when it is discovered with delicate tones it is a real treasure. As it is relatively soft, it is best kept as a collectable or mounted in a pendant or earrings. Occasionally it can be set into rings, usually in a bezel setting so as to prevent the gemstone from being damaged. Amblygonite is said to soothe and relax all who wear the gem. Crystal Healers believe that the gem reduces anxiety and stress, whilst others claim that it assists with creativity and brings dreams to life.

Specimen quality Amblygonite is found in several counties around the world including the UK, France and Germany: however gem-quality material (as far as I know) is currently only being mined in Minas Gerais, Brazil.

American Influences

Firstly let's start by saying that Americans spell the word used to describe items worn for personal adornment differently. What is known as jewellery in England is spelt "jewelry" in the USA.

Prior to the First World War, clothing and jewellery trends in the UK were created on home soil, with only a little influence from European neighbours. However, by the 1940s American culture was very dominant in Europe.

The influence of Hollywood movies and the prominence of film stars set the fashion in jewellery, make-up, hair and clothes. It was widely believed that Hollywood glamour would rub off on you if you had similar clothes and jewellery, so many in Europe wanted look-a-like copies of outfits and jewellery worn by their screen idols.

World War II in Europe halted production of fine jewellery when metals were rationed. Fine precious metal and gem jewellery was simply not available. Quality costume jewellery, which was flourishing in America, became much more acceptable in Europe. Today however, most jewellery fashion trends often start in Europe. Italy, France, Switzerland and the UK seem to have a greater influence on designs around the globe than those starting in the USA. Probably one of the biggest trends to originate in the USA in more recent times is the rebirth of the Celtic twisted cable, as used in David Yurman designs.

Amethyst Throughout history, Amethyst has been one of the most popular and mystical of all gemstones.

Its use in very rudimentary jewellery can be traced back as far as the Neolithic period (approximately 4000BC), and samples of it set into gold rings have been uncovered in burial sites from around 2400BC.

Amethyst is the name given to purple Quartz and some believe that its name derives from the Greek word "Amethustos", "A" meaning "not" and "methustos" meaning "to intoxicate".

In ancient times, wealthy lords who wanted to stay sober were said to have had drinking glasses or goblets made from Amethyst. While pouring wine for their guests they could serve themselves water, as the dark purple hue of the gem would disguise the colour of the drink so it looked like wine, thus allowing the lord appear to be partaking in a tipple! Following the same theme, it was thought in ancient times if you wished to save a drunkard from delirium you could mix crushed Amethyst into a person's drink.

One legend from Greek mythology tells the tale of Dionysus, the god of intoxication, and a young beautiful maiden, named Amethystos, who

Stunning colours of Amethyst are already present in crystform in this Geode.

refused his advances. Dionysus let loose fierce tigers while Amethystos was on her way to pray to the goddess Diana. Before they reached her, Diana turned her into a statue of pure Crystalline Quartz to protect her from the advancing tigers. Humbled by Amethystos' resolution, and horrified at what he had almost done to her, he wept tears of wine. Legend says his tears turned the colourless Quartz purple, thus creating Amethyst.

Amethyst is mentioned in the Old Testament as one of the twelve stones representing the twelve tribes of Israel and was also one of the twelve gemstones adorning the breastplate of the high priest Aaron (Exodus 39). With its association with piety and celibacy, Amethyst has been set into rings and worn by Cardinals, Bishops and Priests of the Catholic Church since the Middle Ages. Over the years, along with its use by the Church, the gem has also been cherished by royalty and several pieces can be found in the British Crown Jewels. Amethyst was also known as a personal favourite of Catherine the Great.

A bracelet worn by Queen Charlotte of England in the early 1700s was valued at £200 at that time. With inflation that would make it more expensive than the 2007 Diamond Skull created by Damien Hirst! However, shortly after this period a new discovery of Amethyst deposits was made in Brazil, which dramatically reduced the value of the Queen's bracelet.

This provides a good example of how the value of genuine gemstones (just like the stock market) can go up and down based on supply and demand. When mines are eventually exhausted prices tend to increase; as new deposits are found, gemstone prices generally decrease.

Amethyst occurs in many shades, from a light, slightly lavender pinkish to a deep purple similar to that of the Cabernet Sauvignon grape. Amethyst

is also pleochroic, which means that when light hits the gem, shades of different colours such as reds and blues can be seen from different angles.

As there is no single dominant organisation or ruling body relating to gemstones, there are often different approaches to how a gem is graded or named. Many organisations within the jewellery industry for instance refer to Green Quartz as Green Amethyst, while others refer to Green Quartz as Prasiolite, Amegreen or Vermarine! This is a really hot topic in the gem world: some believing that the name Amethyst can only be applied to purple Quartz, others saying if a Quartz's green colour is derived from heat treated Amethyst then it should be named Green Amethyst and others saying it should be known as Green Quartz or Prasiolite.

Most Green Amethyst has been available since the mid 1950s, has come from Brazil and is heat treated and irradiated to produce an electrifying transparent olive-coloured green gemstone. That said, Green Amethyst (or whatever you want to call it!), has been known to appear naturally in a small mine in Silesia, Poland, and claims of natural Green Amethyst discoveries have also been made in Namibia, Nevada USA, Zambia and Tanzania.

Different tones of Amethyst have different prefixes: "Siberian Amethyst" refers to darker Amethyst regardless of whether they are from Siberia or not, normally having a tone of 75-80%; and Amethyst with a more pinkish tone (20-30%) is named "Rose De France". Amethyst is a hard and durable gemstone measuring 7 on the Mohs scale. In its rough state, the gem often forms in long prismatic crystals, making it ideal for cutting. Because its colour can often appear banded, it is usually cut into round brilliant shapes which helps the gem display a more uniformed colour when viewed through the table or crown facets.

Amethyst is considered a symbol of peace of mind, modesty and piety. Some believe that Amethyst holds powers to change anger to tranquillity and is used by crystal healers to revert negative energy into positive energy. It is popular for its healing and meditative powers, and purifies the mind, body and spirit, helping to realign the chakras. It is also considered an ideal gemstone for those struggling or recovering from alcoholism as it protects against drunkenness.

Amethyst is the birthstone of February. It is also associated with the zodiac signs of Pisces, Aries, Aquarius and Sagittarius. The gem is mined in several countries including the USA, Brazil, Madagascar and Kenya. One of the largest Amethyst mines in the world is in Maissau in Austria and is unusual in that it is open to the public. If you want to travel further, then the Amethyst mines in Brazil are considered to be the best in the world and as long as you don't mind roughing it a little, you're sure to have a great adventure visiting the local artisan miners.

Miners entering the Uruguai mine.

Amethyst Feature
Alto Uruguai Amethyst

In 2011 I travelled to southern Brazil to visit the small Amethyst mines at Alto Uruguia to learn more about the origin of some of the world's most glorious Amethyst.

In the southern region of Brazil, only 200 miles north of the Uruguayan border lies one of the finest discoveries of Amethyst on the planet in the state of Rio Grande. Alto Uruguai is a hilly district in Rio Grande do Sul (the southernmost state of Brazil) the area is very rural and sparsely populated, with most people living in isolated farmhouses on small farms. The mining area's name is taken from the great river "Rio Uruguai" which travels through Southern Brazil dividing the two states of Santa Catarina and Rio Grande do Sul and then forms part of the border with Uruguay and Argentina.

The warm, temperate climate is good for arable farming, with the main crops being soya, maize and beans. What of course interests us the most is what happens under the soil in Alto Uruguia: the discovery of gorgeous Amethyst with vivid colour and great clarity. The area is not just famed for its purple Amethyst, but also Amethyst

that when irradiated turns a stunning green colour (also known as Prasiolite) and breathtaking Lavender Quartz.

Alto Uruguia Amethyst was formed just before the Jurassic Period when large masses of volcanic lava were flowing from low lying volcanic activity in Southern Brazil. Often trees would get swept along with the lava and over many years these would rot inside the solidified lava and form large pockets (known in geology as vugs). Other pockets were formed in the lava by gas bubbles. Then over a period of thousands of years a hydrothermal process (the movement of hot water) mixed with a cocktail of elements such as iron stopped to rest in these large pockets and formed geodes. Whilst at first glance you would easily overlook their dull grey outer, once cracked open some geodes have a beautiful coloured interior. When did this geological wonder occur? Well, it was during the Cretaceous Period (hence the word cretaceous rock) which started in the Jurassic Period 144 million years ago and is believed to have ended approximately 65 million later.

All of the mines in the region are underground and are mined by small teams, using a combination of explosives, pneumatic drills, hammers and chisels. Many of the tunnels are around two metres high, just enough height to get small carts and basic trucks inside to extract the ore. We all know the jeep stands for "just enough essential parts", well the truck in the picture on the previous page which miners use to get to the rock face takes the meaning to different level! Mining in the area is a very slow process, as the rock in which the geodes are found is incredibly strong. Depending on its size, once a geode has been discovered the actual extraction process can take several days.

Ametrine

Discovered only at the Anahi Mine in Bolivia comes a gemstone with a beautiful split personality.

Ametrine is possibly one of the most interesting and beautiful gemstones to become available on the global gem market during recent years.

Currently only found at the Anahi Mine in Eastern Bolivia, it is a fusion of the gorgeous regal purple of Amethyst and the warm sunshine hue of Citrine, beautifully combined in one stone. In the gem industry, Ametrine also goes by the name of Bolivianite, due the location of its source.

Ametrine's bi-coloured effect is uniquely created due to differing temperatures across the gem during its crystal formation. The area with the highest temperature forms golden Citrine yellows and the cooler zone forms lilac Amethyst colours. However, this one-off occurrence was a tough trick for Mother Nature to perform, because if too much heat had been applied the entire gem would have become a Citrine.

Many gemstone dealers have tried to emulate this balancing act by heating one end of an Amethyst. However they are all said to have failed as the heat travels too fast through the gem, making it all turn to Citrine. Cutting the rough of Ametrine is such an important task because it can make or break the beauty of the gem. Usually the lapidarist (a person who cuts and facets gemstones) will cut the gem into longer shapes so as to draw the eye's attention to its unique bi-colours. The gem looks gorgeous in baguette, emerald and octagon cuts.

Many crystal healers believe that Ametrine holds the same metaphysical properties as both Amethyst and Citrine. It will help guide you through meditation, relieves the stress and strain of everyday life and helps to remove negative emotions and prejudices.

During the last 30 years, the gem trade has favoured Ametrine where the split has been 50/50. Only when there was an equal proportion of Amethyst to Citrine were the prices inflated. Today, in a world where individualism is more prevalent than conformism (we no longer all wear the same branded jumper with the big logo on the front as we did in the '80s) the old rules of the 50/50 split have disappeared.

Now, we consider the vividness of the colour, the clarity of the Ametrine, the cut of the gem more importantly than the percentage of each colour.

More recently, lapidarists have been cutting Ametrine and deliberately selecting areas where the chocolate wrapper purple of the Amethyst portion swirls, wraps and carelessly merges with the sunflower yellows of the Citrine portion. In Hong Kong where a lot of Ametrine is cut and faceted, they have even invented a new name for this style: "Sunburst Ametrine".

Ametrine Feature
The Anhai Mine

The Anhai Mine is located in Santa Cruz, which is just 20 miles from Bolivia's border with Brazil. The Anhai Mine is the only significant source of natural Ametrine on the planet. The mine is owned by Mr Ramiro Rivero and although we have not yet met personally, Ram is a very good friend of my buddy Rob Weldon, who was born in Bolivia and who works at the GIA as their professional photographer.

Rob and I spent a few days together recently on a mining trip in Southern Brazil and during the trip Rob explained to me all about the operation at Anahi…

Ram's plot of land covers some 6200 acres and is located very near to some of the most beautiful rainforests in the world. Historically the land belonged to the Ayoreo (pronounced "ai-o-reo") who were nomadic hunter-gatherers. All of the mining is now done underground in a network of tunnels similar to the Cruzerio Mine in Minas Gerais. The mine's geologists and mining engineers use all of the latest technology in order to extract their valuable treasure and have a well-educated and highly-skilled team of approximately 70 people. As the location is so remote, they recently built a small grass landing strip next to the mine, making it easier for the mine owners to frequently get in and out of the mine. Prior to this they had to travel for eight hours up the Paraguay River by boat, and then make a three hour truck ride through dense jungle forests.

In addition to its world-famous natural Ametrine, the Anahi mine also unearths small amounts of Amethyst, Citrine and Anahite (also known as Lavender Quartz). The mine is operated with great care to the environment and the owners are said to be working towards a carbon neutral status.

Ammolite A kaleidoscope of iridescent colours displayed on the outside of a fossil and from just one small location on the planet - now that's rare!

Ammolite is claimed by many to be the rarest gemstone on the planet. Whilst this might be taking it a little far, it is certainly incredibly rare and to-date has only ever been discovered in the isolated region of Southern Alberta, Canada.

If you were to ask me to categorise its rarity, I would put it on a par with Zultanite and Paraiba Tourmaline. The problem with Ammolite doesn't stop with its rarity and just like Zultanite, taking the rough material and converting it into a piece that can be set into jewellery is a real lapidarist's challenge.

Whilst with Zultanite the difficulty is due to its crystal structure having perfect cleavage, Ammolite is very delicate and only forms in wafer thin microscopic layers. Whilst we are talking about the similarities with Zultanite, there is one more! Both gemstones are two of the last gemstones to be credited with an official gemstone status. But before we go into this in more detail, let me explain exactly how this incredibly iridescent gemstone was formed.

You may remember studying Ammonites at school; these are one of the most instantly recognised forms of fossils to be found on the planet. Ammonites looked something similar to a squid and their habitat was warm tropical waters. Along with dinosaurs, they became extinct around 65 million years ago at the end of the Mesozoic Era. The gemstone Ammolite is found on the upper shell of the Ammonite fossil, but only on those found in Southern Alberta. This sort of explains its rarity: here is a gemstone that can only be found attached to a fossil and only on a particular type of fossil that came to rest in just one location. According to local miners, even once they find an Ammonite in the region, only 5% demonstrate any iridescence and of these, only a tiny percentage are of gem quality!

Back in the Mesozoic Era there was a warm tropical sea area known today as the Western Interior Seaway. Due to the movement of tectonic plates this no longer exists and the area is now some 500 miles from the Canadian coastline. As the sea receded and turned to land the Ammonites became buried in a layer of sediment containing the mineral Bentonite. It was the presence of this mineral in this one location that preserved the wonderful iridescence of the shell and which prevented it from becoming a normal calcite fossil.

The gem is found near the extremely remote town of Magrath, in an area located near the Red Deer River and the St Mary's River in southern Alberta (the nearest major city is Lethbridge). According to folklore the gem was first discovered by a lady who was part of a Blackfoot Indian Tribe. During a very harsh winter, all of the buffalo disappeared and whilst searching for firewood in deep snow, she came across the gemstone under a cottonwood tree. As she held the gem a spirit contacted her and told her it would act as a powerful talisman and would bring the buffalo back to the tribe.

Sure enough, the very next day, buffalos were seen near the tribe's camp. Even today, members of the Blackfoot Tribe wrap the gemstone in buffalo hide and use the gem in ritual ceremonies before they go hunting.

So it's incredibly rare, has a great history, but what's it physically like? Well, I mentioned at the very beginning that the layer of Ammolite is incredibly thin. It is also very soft measuring just 4.5 to 5.5 on the Mohs scale. It's also very brittle and very flaky, and will also bleach if exposed to sunlight for long periods. Not the sort of information you want to hear if you're a miner and have just

uncovered a piece in the earth! Here is a gemstone that has the appearance of the Northern Lights crossed with a Boulder Opal, it has beautiful patterns like spiders webs and is visually one of the prettiest natural items on the planet, but it's not going to last. Luckily this is the age of modern technology, where we have the ability to preserve real treasures. By delicately removing the thin layer from the Ammonite and re-bonding it to a pre-cut slice of the original fossil and then by topping the gem in transparent natural Quartz, the gem becomes preserved. The Quartz on the top of this triplet is sometimes cut with either parallel bars or checkerboard facets. The interaction of the surface lustre of these facets with the colour play of the gemstone beneath can result in some of the most mesmerising optical effects that you will ever see in a gemstone.

Because the gemstone is normally sold as a triplet, it is not sold by carat weight as this would be very misleading, instead it is valued by its size and its play of colour. The more vibrant the colours and the more kaleidoscopic it is, the more expensive it becomes. Just like Tanzanite and Diamonds have a fairly recognised grading system, so do Ammolites. The very finest Ammolite is graded AA and there are three other grades of A+, A and A-.

Some Ammolites will show just one colour and these tend to be graded either A or A-. For every different colour you see in an Ammolite, you are actually seeing into the gemstone and looking at different layers. Colour derived by iridescence as is the case with Ammolite, is different to the colour of most gemstones where the colour seen is the result of absorption of light. With Ammolite each colour is actually being returned to the eye by the reflection of different layers. The more layers there are, the more colours you will see. When you see reds and greens you are looking at light bouncing back from thicker layers in the structure, whilst the thinner layers

deliver mainly blues and violets. Because these layers are never clearly defined, every single Ammolite will look different, each one with its own multi-coloured fingerprint of nature.

Just like Tanzanite, Zultanite and Larimar, Ammolite is only found in one location on the planet. Similar to claims by the biggest mining organizations in all of these single location discoveries, is that Ammolite will run out in the near future. The biggest mining company Korite International go as far as to claim that Ammolite will run out in 20 years time: now that sounds kind of familiar!

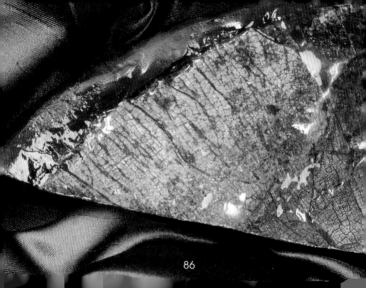

Ammolite Mining

Tom is not your normal gem adventurer. He is a quietly spoken, gentle and very sweet, yet professional type of guy. That's not to say all gem prospectors are loud and aggressive, but in the main the type of people who decide to pump a load of cash into the ground in a vain hope they will hit a vein of gems (sorry for the pun) tend to be just slightly nuts!

I have probably just offended lots of my mining friends who will read this book, but they know it's true: gem prospectors are gamblers, they live on the edge and always believe tomorrow will be the day they unearth the big gem.

Tom is a great guy; very calm and very calculating. He first started his Ammolite business with a bunch of friends who loved abseiling. One day as they descended down a hill top in Alberta, Canada, one of them noticed as the sun shone over his shoulder a kaleidoscope of colour nestled between two pieces of rock. He halted his descent, pulled out his pen knife and was amazed at the multi-coloured stone that he had extracted.

A few days later he showed it to Tom. Instantly Tom knew what it was as he was familiar with the gemstone mining of Ammolite in the region. Over the following months Tom sent his friends

87

back to the rock face and every now and then they managed to unearth several gorgeous pieces. Tom then set about learning how to turn this incredible multi-coloured, ancient fossil into a valuable gemstone. He hired several lapidarists who had experience of working with this fossilised gem and set about launching his own collection.

In 2010 I met up with Tom and we agreed to represent him in the UK. This, from my point of view, was pretty much a no-brainer decision for me, because over the years I had seen people selling Ammolite in the UK, also mined in this same area for incredibly high prices. I knew as I was dealing direct with the miner I would be able to bring Ammolite to my customers at the lowest prices the world had ever seen.

Earlier this year Tom managed to obtain an official mining licence from the local government to mine an area which is half a mile square. Tom laughs as he tells me that the largest Ammolite mining company has to cross his plot in order to reach their mine. Tom then explained how the licences work. Every single fossil they unearth, they have to send a photo to the local museum, with written details on the piece. The government basically have first refusal on any fossil that they feel is of historical or scientific value. Tom explains that they tend to be very reasonable and that he gets to keep nearly all of the pieces he uncovers.

The land he rents is actually allocated to the Hutterite colony. One of the beliefs of this very religious group is that they should not have their photographs taken. Tom explained that they just recently lost a court case where they had refused to even have their photos taken for their driving licences. Tom said that they were really kind-hearted people and that they would frequently drop by his mine and give him a bottle of their homemade rhubarb wine.

Tom has recently bought a huge 90 ton Catapillar digger and has just started excavation. As of yet, very little has been found, but as all mine owners often do, he tells me that his pay dirt is just around the corner.

His licence is very strict and Tom has to ensure that when he finishes his expedition, he has to invest in turning the land back to its previous condition. This of course is a huge gamble, as even though there has been Ammolite discovered in the region, there is no concrete proof that Tom will discover it on the strip of land that he has leased.

In the meantime his two good friends continue to abseil down the hillside to ensure that he has enough pieces to supply me every now and then.

Andalusite This Spanish treasure is undeniably one of the most highly pleochoric gems created by nature.

Andalusite is a transparent to translucent gem that derives its name from Andalusia in Spain where it was first discovered.

The gem is actually a polymorph of two gem varieties: Sillimanite and the hugely popular Kyanite. This means they are identical in chemical composition but differ in crystal structure.

Andalusite is often mistaken for Smokey Quartz, Chrysoberyl or Tourmaline. The gemstone benefits from a very distinct and attractive pleochroism, which lapidarists try to highlight when faceting the gem. Usually, when cutting strongly pleochroic gemstones (Iolite,

90

Tanzanite, Kunzite, etc.), lapidarists typically try to minimize the pleochroism and maximize the single most attractive colour. Interestingly, Andalusite is the opposite, as all the colours visible in different directions are attractive. Cutters therefore try to orient the gem to get a pleasing mix of its orange, brown, yellow, green and golden colours. When cut successfully, Andalusite looks unlike any other gemstone, displaying patterns of colour dancing around its facets

Andalusite registers 7.5 on the Mohs scale, and in addition to Spain has been discovered in Switzerland, Sri Lanka, Kenya, Mozambique and the USA.

Andesine What an interesting world we live in! I have always explained to my jewellery team that you should never state anything about gemstones as an absolute fact and instead should use phrases such as 'currently one of the rarest gemstones on the planet' or 'sources inform us that the gem will no longer be mined within the next 10 years'.

Remember they used to say Garnet comes in every single colour apart from blue, but then what did they discover in Madagsascar in 1998? You guessed it!

It's so easy to get carried away in an industry where people state things as fact, but in reality this industry should by now, after trading coloured gemstones for over 5,000 years, have begun to realise that Mother Nature is never predictable and often seems to do things that make even the world's best gem experts occasionally look a little silly.

In 2002 at the world famous Tucson Gem Show in Arizona, when a stunning new gemstone called Andesine exploded on to the scene (well, it wasn't brand new, but we will come to that in a moment), there were many stories and myths surrounding its original location and what in fact the gemstone was.

The gemstone is so stunning that the miners of this new source kept its location a real secret and many in the industry incorrectly said that it came from either India or the Democratic Republic of Congo. With so much demand for top quality Andesine, many in the industry were selling very similar pieces and claiming it was from the same source as the very finest material, and as nobody knew exactly where the new source was, nobody could dispute the dealers' claims of origin. Whilst many were uncertain of the location of this new magnificent gemstone, it was certainly being mined somewhere in the Himalayas, a far cry from where it was originally discovered in the 1840s in the Andes Mountains in Bolivia, from where its name is derived. But what is this gemstone and what is its real name?! Unfortunately, this is still a matter for debate. Firstly a fact: the gemstone is a top quality red gemstone and is a member of the Feldspar family. The finest examples are right up there with Paraiba Tourmaline and Alexandrite. In fact, Andesine shares similarities with both in that there is also a green colour change version of the gemstone which appears very similar to Alexandrite and like Paraiba, part of its magical brilliance is due to the presence of Copper.

At the 2008 Olympic Games held

in Beijing, there was a large display featuring many pieces of Red Andesine which had been chosen as the official gemstone of the games. This raised alarm bells in the industry, as it was believed that very little of the gem had ever been discovered in China and Tibet.

On the 31st of January 2011 at the Gemstone Industry Laboratory Conference (the GILC is the most important meeting in the gem trade calendar relating to the technical aspects of our industry), the forty or so delegates spent two hours discussing a recent trip to the Andesine mines of Tibet by several respected members of the trade. Here, we were informed that the group had travelled to the highlands of the Himalayas in Southern Tibet to the Bainang County, which is located some 45 miles south of Tibet's second largest city, Xigaze. The road from the city is nothing more than a dirt track and the group had to ascend to 4000 metres above sea level. In the winter the track is impossible to travel as it is deep under snow and even when the team arrived during the summer they said the air was frigid and very thin due to the altitude.

At the remote area where the mines are located, several families have now set up home. During the time spent in the area, the team did indeed uncover some pieces of natural Red Andesine themselves, but only saw around 10 gem miners in the whole region. The fact that there were so few miners in this remote location led the team to believe that although they had proven that Red Andesine can be found naturally in Tibet, it could not be the only source of the gem.

So where is the majority of Red Andesine being unearthed? The answer lies in Inner Mongolia. This is a country that is landlocked: to its north is Russia and to the east, south and west is China. In terms of geographical size, the country is the 19th largest country in the world spanning a huge 604,000 square miles, yet its population is only 2.9 million. That's the equivalent of the population of Birmingham being spread across a country six times bigger than Great Britain. To the north of the city of Baotou is the small county of Guyang: here in the small villages of Shuiquan and Haibouzi for many years local miners have been excavating small quantities of fine yellow Andesine (some call it Yellow Labradorite as both are plagioclase Feldspars). Since 2003, the main mine just outside of the village has been run by Wang Gou Ping. At the end of each year's harvest, Wang hires 40 or so farmers to mine for the treasured Yellow Andesine. Many of these golden glowing gems are then treated with diffusion and then turn orangeish red, looking very similar to those coming out of Tibet. What are the main differences between Andesine coming from these very different locations, other than one is colour enhanced? As they say in the wine trade, the 'terroir' is very different, a term which expresses the particular characteristic bestowed by the geographical, geological and climate conditions. In Tibet the gems are mined at 4000 metres above sea level, whereas in Mongolia the landscape is very flat. In terms of chemical composition, the gems from Tibet have a lower Ba/Li ratio than those discovered in Mongolia, but have a natural presence of copper.

The conclusion reached from the dedicated work of the team that went to both Tibet and Mongolia in 2010, is that their natural Red Andesine is being mined in Tibet, but the quantities are extremely small. The vast majority of Red Andesine on the market we now believe to have come from Mongolia and has had its colour transformed from a sunflower yellow to a beautiful orangish red colour through diffusion.

When it comes to Green Andesine and Colour Change Andesine, these are incredibly rare and beautiful gems also. The colour change variety has some

Andradite Garnet You will see from the gem table that Andradite has quite a complex chemical composition.

The gem receives its wide variety of colours due to the fact that its complex composition can be a cocktail of manganese, aluminium, titanium or chromium.

There are three main members of the Andradite family of Garnets: Melanite is the black variety of the gem and is not that often seen in jewellery. Its main ingredient is titanium and it is often discovered near volcanoes and in particular old lava deposits.

Topazolite is normally yellow in colour and receives its name for its similarity in appearance to Imperial Topaz. The gem has been discovered in Italy and the Swiss canton of Valais, however it is incredibly rare and very hard these days to find.

Demantoid, the green member of Andradite, is a gemstone that is regarded by many as one of the most collectable of all.

The gem group was named after the Brazilian mineralogist José Bonifácio de Andrade e Silva, who in the 1830s discovered four new minerals. It is also found in Italy, Switzerland, Norway, Mexico and USA.

Angelite Recently I received a very excited phone call from a good friend of mine who was in Peru! 'What are you doing in Peru?' I asked him. I thought he must be on holiday as there is very little gem mining in the country. It turned out that one of his friends had just discovered a small deposit of gemstones and had called him in for his opinion.

What had been discovered was a gemstone known as Angelite which is a delicious lilac, pale blue gem variety of Anhydrite (a gem formed from the compression on Celestite over a period of millions of years), so named for its angelic appearance. Anhydrite can also be found in white, grey, blue, pink and red, but only the lilac-coloured variety is known as 'Angelite'. Despite the common occurrence of Anhyrdite, good quality specimens are extremely rare. It is also a fairly new gemstone, having only been discovered in 1987 in Peru.

On the very rare occasion, you may find a piece that is green and similar in appearance to Malachite.

Its hardness of 3.5 on the Mohs scale coupled with its orthorhombic crystal structure makes it ideal for carving figurines and beaded jewellery. In fact, it is believed that the Ancient

Egyptians used the Anhydrite rock to carve animal figurines.

Angelite does have a few drawbacks as a gemstone. First it is a little softer than most gemstones, so you need to be careful if you are wearing different gemstones and metals alongside it.

Secondly it should not be immersed in water for long periods or come into contact with chemicals otherwise it may turn into gypsum (incidentally the second softest mineral on the Mohs scale). In fact its name is derived from the Greek phrase 'an hydros' which means without water, as the gemstone is formed when the mineral Gypsum has formed without water and crystallised. When it comes to cleaning it is best just to use a damp cloth or better still a soft jewellery cloth.

So if it has a few drawbacks why is it so hugely popular? The answer is simple: it is both extremely beautiful and is reported to have many healing benefits.

Some people have reported optical properties including an internal play of light, and some specimens fluorescing under UV light.

Throughout this book you will have noticed that we do not talk about crystal healing too much, preferring to concentrate more on the background and technical aspects of gems. However, with Angelite it's hard to ignore some of these beliefs as they appear quite constant regardless of whom you talk to or whichever book or website you read. Now that might be because everyone is copying each other's research and if that is the case let me apologise for jumping on the bandwagon! Healers use Angelite to unblock energy pathways and to balance the thyroid. It is also highly regarded by crystal healers as assisting with communication with other humans, including those who are no longer with us.

I have also read that Angelite is very useful for weight control and although my wife (who is very slim) has yet to wear the gem, in her previous career as a pop singer her stage name was coincidently Angelle!

The gem is believed to be related to the fifth chakra (throat), which helps with communication. Angelite is said to provide the wearer with a heightened awareness and to help one focus on kindness and brotherhood. It is said to promote compassion and understanding and to alleviate psychological pain.

As well as Peru, Angelite has also been found in Germany and New Mexico.

Annabella
*Every piece
of Annabella
jewellery is
handcrafted to the
finest detail and
features genuine
gemstones set in
beautiful flowing
silver designs.*

YEAR	GEMSTONE
1	ANY GEM SET IN GOLD
2	GARNET
3	PEARL
4	BLUE TOPAZ
5	SAPPHIRE
6	AMETHYST
7	ONYX
8	TOURMALINE
9	LAPIS LAZULI
10	DIAMOND
11	TURQUOISE

YEAR	GEMSTONE
12	JADE
13	CITRINE
14	OPAL
15	RUBY
16	IMPERIAL TOPAZ & PERIDOT
17	AMETHYST
18	GARNET
19	AQUAMARINE
20	EMERALD
21	IOLITE
22	SPINEL

Anniversary Gemstones

Anniversaries are traditionally celebrated with the giving of gifts relating to the year of the wedding, civil partnerships or indeed any memorable event.

Around the turn of the 19th century it was popular to give gifts of paper, cotton or leather for the first few years of marriage. However, in more recent times and due to the increasing popularity of fine, rare gemstones, it is more popular to give jewellery to the one you love.

Most people know of the major anniversary gemstones such as Pearl for 30 years, Ruby for 40 and Diamond for 50, but did you know there is in fact a gemstone for every year up to 25 years?

Although there are several variations for a few of the anniversaries, the table on the right details those we believe to be the most universally adopted.

This list of gemstones to celebrate the day that two people made a life time commitment to one another is reported to have been collated by the American National Association of Jewellers in 1912. Since the list was compiled there have been very few discoveries of new gemstones. When you consider how much the world has changed over the past 100 years, its quite comforting to know that one thing remains pretty constant, and that is our love affair with gemstones. However, there has been one major discovery, a discovery that stopped people talking of the big four gemstones and made them increase this to the big five and that is of course Tanzanite. As with the official list of Birthstones which has been modified to include Tanzanite as a December Birthstone, the Anniversary list has added Tanzanite as the 24th Wedding Anniversary gemstone.

For the first 25 years of marriage there is a gemstone or precious metal assigned to each year and thereafter for every fifth year. Notice also how the list still retains precious metals for the 1st, 25th and 50th wedding anniversaries. If you were able to celebrate your 80th anniversary (bearing in mind there have only been a handful of people who have reached this), just think of all the beautiful jewellery you could acquire, and what better reason for it?!

One of the loveliest emails I ever received from a gentleman (stay with me on this one!), was from someone who had found our website while searching on Google to find an anniversary present for his wife. He admitted to have known nothing about gemstones prior to finding our site, but on seeing that Amethyst was the suggested gift for the 6th Wedding Anniversary, he decided to purchase a ring for his wife. His wife was delighted with the gift and commented on how much thought and research he must have put in to find the most appropriate of gifts and on how much he must have spent! He finished his email by saying that the best thing of all, was that the ring cost less than the bunch of flowers he gave her the year before and that he would be back in 12 months' time to buy Onyx!

YEAR	GEMSTONE
23	IMPERIAL TOPAZ
24	TANZANITE
25	ANY GEM SET IN SILVER
30	PEARL
35	CORAL AND EMERALD
40	RUBY
45	ALEXANDRITE AND SAPPHIRE
50	GOLD
55	ALEXANDRITE AND EMERALD
60	DIAMOND
65	SPINEL
70	SAPPHIRE
75	DIAMOND
80	RUBY

Antique Cushion Cut

One of the most romantic gem cuts of all time

Also known as an "Antique Cut" or "Pillow Cut", the antique cushion cut in appearance is similar to the "Old Mine Cut", which was popular in the late 19th century, and the more modern "Oval Cut".

The Antique Cushion Cut is occasionally used for Diamonds. Although the cut does not have the same ability to display dispersion as the brilliant cut, it is however very romantic in appearance as it is reminiscent of cuts applied to Diamonds worn by previous generations. The cut is often applied to coloured gemstones and can dramatically increase the flashes of lustre seen from the crown of the gem.

Often you may hear the cut being referred to as the Candlelight Cut. The reason for this is that in the early 1900s, before the light bulb was in every home, the Antique Cushion Cut was said to bring out the fire (dispersion) in a Diamond better than any other cut.

During the Art Deco period, the cut was extremely popular in Engagement Rings. The Graff Diamond and the Hope Diamond are both a variation on the Antique Cushion Cut.

Apatite Famous for its swimming pool blues to lively light greens.

Although Apatite is really a family of gemstones, as the individual members have very long and difficult-to-pronounce names, the jewellery industry tends to use Apatite as the generic name.

Historically, because the gem was often confused with other gemstones such as Tourmaline, Peridot and Beryl, its name is derived from the Greek meaning "to deceive".

The more common colours for Apatite are similar to Paraiba Tourmaline, with swimming pool blues through to lively light greens. That said, other colours occasionally occur: colourless to white, brownish-yellow, greyish-green and one known as the "Asparagus stone" due to its resemblance to the vegetable. There is also a 'Cat's Eye Apatite', which is a rarity at Apatite mines. As you would guess from its name, this type of Apatite displays the optical effect of Chatoyancy, an effect caused by tiny fibrous inclusions that are naturally arranged in a parallel configuration. When the light hits the surface of the polished gemstone, a narrow line of light appears, which looks very similar to the opening and closing of a cat's eye.

Finds of Apatite over 1 carat are very rare indeed, and it is also very difficult to find clean Apatite stones over this size, as many will still have a few inclusions. That said, if the colour saturation is good, then even with inclusions you still have yourself a rare and beautiful piece.

The recent finds of Apatite in Madagascar in 1995 have added to the popularity of this gem. Exhibiting excellent saturation, Madagascan Apatite's colours range from neon "Emerald" greens (as typified by our Fort Dauphin Apatite) to neon "Paraiba" blues.

Even rarer than gem-quality Apatite is the purple variation of this gemstone, found in the Mount Apatite of Maine, USA.

Apatite has been associated with many healing properties and is a gemstone often combined with other gems to further its healing powers. It is also thought to be an aid to seeing the truth about oneself.

When you combine Rose Quartz with Apatite it is meant to draw and give unconditional love; if you pair it with colourless Quartz it can help you see the changes that need to occur in your life; and when combined with

Aquamarine it is believed to help you make those changes.

For such a beautiful gemstone, with almost a neon glow, it is difficult to comprehend how many Apatites are created from fossilised dinosaur bones! At just 5 on the Mohs scale, Apatite is one of the softest gems to be set in jewellery, but treated respectably its alluring and luscious glow will keep its owner entranced for many years.

Deposits have been found in several locations including Cornwall in England, Canada, Norway, Russia and Sweden.

2.6mm, w...
al weight given as ...

(WHITE)
generally assessed as SI₁

and diamond crossover/twist set in 18 carat
gold. Gross weight 3.9 grams. Hallmarked
NGHAM 2008 DK - GEMS TV. Centre
eloque cut: a semi-transparent medium green
wing characteristic near/on surface hairline fissures.

Boolutt
Jul 08
£ 147

CONTINUED

Date 10 March 2011

Signed *Simon Hemsted*

...and appraised the articles scheduled *above* and in *my* opinion the figures given represent
...ntified and are valid only for *their stated purpose*. Values given are based on prices
... and in order that *such values* are interpreted correctly it is important that
... the schedule.

...1 40588

...msted

is based on
only for the

KS201

116

Appraisals are a worthwhile investment for your most prized possessions.

I have put appraisals and valuations under two separate headings. The reason for this is that whilst valuations are often sought by people wanting to insure their items, they are not often of a technical nature. Whilst valuations of gold and diamond jewellery can be done on most high streets, there are very few places - certainly in the UK - where you can get a full appraisal of a coloured gemstone. If you are fortunate enough to have inherited jewellery and it is set with beautiful gemstones, you may want to have it professionally appraised, because you may be surprised with what you have.

A good friend of mine who appraises jewellery once had a customer who wanted her beaded necklace valued because it had a nice Emerald on the clasp. She could hardly believe her luck when she was informed that the beads were all very high grade and incredibly rare Imperial Jade and that the piece was worth over £100,000!

If you have a coloured gemstone and want to find out more about it, be sure to go to a coloured gemstone specialist. Make sure they have not only been trained to the highest level in coloured stones, but also make sure they are using up-to-date equipment. The reason why I recommend this is that there are so many treatments and enhancements constantly being developed for gemstones, that unless the appraiser has the latest technology, they may make incorrect assumptions.

A little knowledge is also a dangerous thing and my good friend Glenn Lehrer who is one of the most highly skilled gentlemen in the coloured gemstone industry, tells a wonderful story which highlights the above point. "A lady once walked into my store in San Francisco to have some pieces valued, as she was leaving I noticed she was wearing a lovely ring, so I asked her why she did not want it valued along with her other pieces. She said 'oh, unfortunately this piece is just a synthetic Sapphire but I wear it for sentimental reason.' So I asked her if she minded if I took a look. Even without a loupe, I could tell this Sapphire was in fact genuine. So I politely asked her to remove it so I could view it under a microscope. She looked a little confused with my level of excitement but agreed with my surprising request. Through the lens I could clearly see a pattern of inclusions consistent with either a Burmese or Ceylon Sapphire. I asked her why she thought it was synthetic and she said that she had once had it valued by a dealer in town who told her it was synthetic.

"I asked her to step behind my counter and have a look for herself in the microscope, I asked her if she could see the patterns of lines and once she acknowledged them for herself, I told her that it was actually a very rare and beautiful coloured Sapphire, which I could tell from my observations had not even been heat treated. It was worth a small fortune."

Now as Glenn lives in San Fransisco, you might find it uneconomical to send your pieces to him for appraisal, therefore I have listed above some of the best laboratories in Europe.

I had a similar experience only a few months ago: a customer bought a stunning 4.8 carat Tanzanite from us set into 18k gold. She took it to her local jeweller for an evaluation and left the building furious with us as the man in the store said it was not really worth more than £100. However, he liked the design of the piece and was therefore happy to offer her a really good price of £200 for it. The customer left the store in floods of tears and after having a coffee called my office and asked to speak to me directly. After I managed to calm her down I asked her to explain the full story. I looked at her account on our computer and found the full details of what she had purchased. I told her that she was very lucky that she did not sell it. Firstly, I explained to her that even the scrap value of the gold was worth more than £200 to the jeweller! This amazing ring had over half a carat of quality diamonds and the jeweller could probably have sold those in his store for another £800. So already he should have offered her £1000.

Most importantly, the Tanzanite was of a very high grade and without blowing our own trumpet, I find it highly unlikely that there is anyone in the UK that buys as much Tanzanite as we do and could source the gem at a lower price and I could see that we had paid over £900 for the loose gem. I asked the customer to send the piece to a proper lab and gave her the address of several to choose from. I had originally sold her the piece for less than £2000 and so I made her an offer; I said "If you send it to any of these accredited laboratories, and they do not appraise it for more than my company sold it to you, then I will not only pay for the appraisal, but I will take it back and give you a full refund". Interestingly, the customer never called me back!

But what information can you get if you invest in a professional appraisal? Well, firstly you will be informed about the purity of your precious metal (not all gem laboratories automatically do this so if you want your metal assayed it's best to check with them first). Most importantly though, you want to know more about your gem. You want to know if it is genuine, laboratory grown or synthetic. Once that it is established that your gemstone is of a natural origin, you may also like to find out what enhancements it has had. For some gemstones, quality laboratories will often even tell you the most likely country of origin.

Aquamarine is one of the world's most popular and well-known gemstones. Often found with great clarity in a light yet energetic blue.

Aquamarine is a real favourite of many gem collectors and in a world that's becoming more and more polluted, Aquamarine offers us all a breath of fresh air.

A member of the Beryl family, Aquamarine's characteristic pale blue colour is created by the presence of iron. Likewise, all members of the Beryl family obtain their colours by the presence of metallic elements, without which pure Beryl remains colourless.

Gemstones that are coloured by nature in this way are known as allochromatic. Aquamarine's younger sister Morganite is coloured by manganese, and its older and more complicated sister, Emerald, receives her personality from the presence of chromium, iron and vanadium.

Its name is derived from the Latin "aqua" for "water" and "mare" for "sea", and many superstitions and legends regarding the sea have been attached to the gemstone over the years. Believed to be the treasure of mermaids, the gem is said to be especially strong when submerged in water. When its powers seemed to dwindle, the gem would be placed in water on the night of a sparkling full moon.

In times gone by, as a very last resort, sailors caught in a storm were believed to throw their Aquamarines overboard to calm the gods. Sailors were also said to have taken Aquamarine to sea as a lucky charm to protect against shipwreck, and many people today still wear Aquamarine to prevent travel sickness.

Back on shore, Aquamarine is believed to both soothe and prolong relationships, and for this reason is often given as an anniversary gift way before its official listing for one's 19th anniversary. For those frightened of spiders or flying, wearing Aquamarine is said to suppress one's phobias.

Out of the ground, many Aquamarines have a slight green tint and are often heat treated to turn the gem into a more pure blue. However, over recent years, the lighter, natural colour has become very popular amongst gemstone collectors. In either shade, this birthstone for March is highly sought after for its clarity, transparency and undeniable calmness.

Similar to Amethyst where different shades are given different prefixes, Aquamarine also has a different prefix relating to its colour. Santa Maria

Aquamarine describes those with a deeper shade of blue than normal. The name is derived from the Santa Maria de Itabira gem mines of Brazil, where deep and vibrant Aquamarines have been found - not, as some people believe, from the name of the ship on which Christopher Columbus made his first cross Atlantic voyage, or indeed from Santa Maria city in California.

The largest source of Aquamarine is found in the state of Minas Gerais in south-east Brazil, but today Africa is becoming a strong rival, with mining activities in countries such as Madagascar, Mozambique, Nigeria and Tanzania.

Aquamarine receives its colour from the presence of two types of iron, ferrous and ferric. Ferrous iron provides the gem with its trademark blue colour, whilst the presence of ferric iron turns the gem slightly green. Normally in its rough state, as when it is mined, Aquamarine is more of a greenish blue. To remove this secondary colour, the rough is normally heat treated before it is sent for cutting, converting ferric iron to ferrous iron. Unusually, as it does not take a high temperature to purify the colour of Aquamarines, it is undetectable in nearly all laboratory tests. For this reason it is always best to assume that any Aquamarine you purchase has been heat treated. As the

heat treating does not intensify the tone of the Aquamarine (it only turns its green hues to blue) some gem collectors prefer Aquamarines that feature their natural greenish blue colour.

The darker an Aquamarine, the more desirable and valuable it becomes. Normally its tone ranges from just 10 to 30% tone and once into the high twenties it is often referred to as Santa Maria Aquamarine. Some Aquamarines will appear almost colourless in normal daylight and yet display a beautiful tone under the light of a candle or a light bulb; so much so that it is known as an evening gemstone.

Although today the prefix "Martha Rocha" is often used more to describe some of the finest Kunzites, it was initially used as a descriptive word for Aquamarine. In 1954 a huge glowing Aquamarine was discovered in the Brazilian town of Teofilo Otoni and was named after the winner of the Miss Brazil competition that year, whose eyes were said to have been of the same colour.

Argonite is named after the Molina de Aragon mine in Guadalajara, Spain where the gem was discovered in 1788 (the mine is situated close to the town of Aragon).

Aragonite is a unique mineral gemstone, as it has the same chemical composition also found in organic molluscs. The crystal structure of Aragonite is also very unusual in that it is often found in needle-like, six-sided prisms.

In addition to its initial discovery in Spain, three large Aragonite caves have also been discovered in Slovakia, Mexico and Argentina.

The cave in Slovakia is buried deep in the Slovak Metalliferous Mountains between Jelsava and Stitnik. Known as the Ochtinska Aragonite Cave, it was discovered in 1954 and was opened to the public in 1972. Unlike most public caves full of stalactites or stalagmites, the unusual crystal structure of Aragonite resembles small shrubs and bushes. One of the main attractions at the mine is the Milky Way Hall, where Aragonites high in the ceiling shine like the stars in the Milky Way. In gemstone terms, the Aragonite in the mine is fairly young; dating back just

13,000 to 100,000 years.

Crystal healers believe that Golden Aragonite is important to the 3rd Chakra and White Aragonite benefits the 7th. I also read Aragonite is suggested as a healer for painful knees.
pleochroism,

Art Deco It was the age of jazz, prohibition and the Charleston. Queen Victoria was no longer on the throne, but countless ideals and influences from her age still remained.

It was the 1920s, and the world was about to see a profound new style that would change history forever. The style would be known as Art Deco. It was bold, lavish and elegant and was to radically change the art world, leaving a lasting impression that can still be seen today.

After the Universal Exposition of 1900, a group of French artists created a formal collective which was known as 'Société des Artistes Décorateurs' (The Society of the Decorator Artists) of Paris.

Not entirely of their making, the Art Deco 'movement' began more as an amalgamation of numerous different styles and movements of the early 1900s. Art Deco affected architecture, painting, film, both interior and industrial design, and, most importantly, fashion. Jewellery that came out of the Art Deco movement was forward thinking and extremely bold. Its "in your face" style represented the fast modernization of the world around it.

Art Deco made vast use of triangular,

angular and geometric shapes, employing symmetry and repetition. The movement attempted to combine mass production with high-quality art and design. Tiaras, cameos and lavalieres from the Victorian era were now unpopular, and gave way to fashionable cocktail rings, long pendants and bangle bracelets.

Accessories became popular again: elaborately detailed cigarette cases and ladies compacts were all ornately jewelled and became just as important as earrings, necklaces and bangles. Inexpensive stones such as Coral and crystal were used with platinum and gold. It has been suggested that this opulent and lavish style was a reaction to the hard times and rationing of WW1.

The fundamental difference that made the Art Deco period so extraordinary was that the same design ideas put into jewellery were also being engineered in buildings, ships and even household appliances.

Diamonds began to be cut in new and exciting shapes never seen before. Many of these, such as pear cut, emerald cut and marquise cut were extremely similar to the cuts we see today. These new-found gem cuts blended in with the symmetrical and geometrical nature of the jewellery itself.

Colour played an important role in the Art Deco movement: everything became bold, vibrant and vivid. The way colour was applied was often dramatic; reacting to the light, neutral colours used during the previous Art Nouveau period. Gemstones such as Ruby, Emerald, Sapphire, and Coral became popular for this reason.

Art Nouveau -
(1880 - 1914)

Art Nouveau was a rich, decorative and poignant era. Its objective was not to imitate, but to evoke.

Beginning in the later years of Queen Victoria's rule, and carrying on well into the 20th century, the name of the movement 'Art Nouveau' comes from 'Maison de l'Art Nouveau', a shop in Paris that displayed art of this design. The words 'Art Nouveau' are French and simply mean 'New Art'.

Although the movement as a whole lasted about 35 years, the period in which jewellery was created in this style was much shorter lived; only lasting about fifteen years. However, its influence is not to be underestimated as it has gone on to inspire many styles for years after its original popularity decreased.

Art Nouveau was groundbreaking. It marked a time where designers would start looking at the world around them, taking stimuli from the natural world, rather than looking into history for inspiration. The style was a reaction to mass produced jewellery, popular towards the end of the Victorian period. The jewellery was bold, expressive, exotic and exuberant.

When the first few examples of 'Art Nouveau' were showcased in Paris, there was outrage. It represented a radical change, and was different to anything most people had ever seen. Viewers either loved it or despised it. The 'rebellion' was said to have freed a creative energy that had been suppressed for so long.

Art Nouveau incorporated highly stylised designs with flowing, elongated, curving lines. Inspiration came from a wide spectrum, often from nature: ferns, roots, buds, spiders and dragonflies. Snakes became an unlikely popular symbol of life, sexuality and eternity. Unusual designs based on flowers and plants that had not been used before in jewellery were experimented with. Peacocks, and particularly their feathers, became fashionable and were featured in all types of jewellery.

Art Nouveau also used the female form in all its glory, proudly displaying it on necklaces and earrings. The women would have long flowing hair, celebrating the natural woman and her new place in society.

One of the defining techniques of the Art Nouveau period was enamelling. It was used to create patterns or pictures on the desired object, by fusing powdered glass to the surface. The most popular type of enamelling used was known as "Plique a'jour", which gave an effect that has been likened to stained glass. Plique a'jour gave the jewellery a distinct, almost three-dimensional effect, which was unique to the time. It was notoriously hard to do, and was a sign of the artist's skill. Other types of enamelling were 'basse-taille' and 'guilloche.'

NEWHALL STREET

Assay In the UK, it is a legal requirement for all gold jewellery over 1 gram and all silver jewellery over 7.78 grams to be officially hallmarked by the British Assay Office.

There are four main assay offices in the UK; all of whom have their own hallmark. All items assayed in Birmingham have an anchor stamped into them; Sheffield, a Rose; Edinburgh, a castle; and London, a leopard.

The hallmark includes the purity of the metal: 375 being 9k gold; 585 being 14k gold; 750 being 18k gold; and 925 being Sterling Silver. It is also a legal requirement for the hallmark to carry the sponsor's mark; this is normally the initials of the jewellery importer, retailer or the manufacturer.

In the UK there is also an option for the hallmark to carry a year symbol, which is intended to help further generations trace jewellery back to the date their possession was hallmarked.

In the UK the history of assay testing and hallmarking precious metals dates back to 1300. Under the instruction of Edward I, hallmarking became a legal requirement for Pewter, Silver and Gold in order to protect the public against fraud, and to protect legitimate traders against unfair competition.

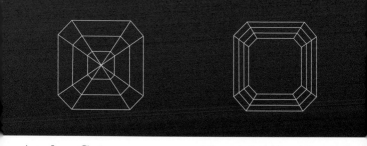

Asscher Cut Introduced by the Asscher Brothers of Holland in 1902, the Asscher cut is also referred to as a square emerald cut.

Just like regular emerald cuts, the Asscher cut has cropped corners and stepped facets running parallel to the girdle, up to the table and down to the culet. Its main difference to an emerald cut is that the table is smaller. This cut was very popular in the 1920s but had gone out of fashion until recent years. Interestingly, this cut has been featured in 'Sex and the City' and has been used for many celebrity engagement rings.

The Asscher brothers were famous Diamond cutters in Holland: they were the founders of the Royal Asscher Diamond Company in 1854. The brothers were both entrusted to cut the famous Cullinan Diamond by King Edward VII in 1907.

It is reported that the Asscher brothers studied the Diamond for three months before any work was carried out. Eventually Joseph Asscher, who was under extreme pressure due to being tasked with shaping the biggest Diamond in the world, took his cleaving knife and hammer to the rough Diamond. To his horror, his first strike completely broke the cleaving knife,

but luckily the Diamond remained undamaged! At the second attempt, the Diamond split perfectly in two.

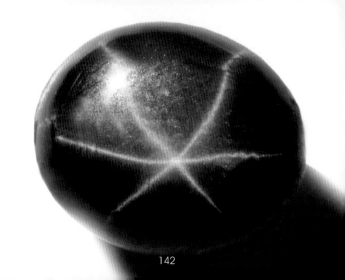

142

Asterism An optical phenomenon displayed mainly in certain translucent to opaque Sapphires and Rubies, whereby a four or six ray star seems to appear beneath the surface of the gem, which will normally float across the surface as the light source moves.

To observe the effect it is best to view a gem under a single light source and slowly rock the gem. The star is caused by "tube like" fibrous inclusions, which are all arranged parallel to one another. Prior to shining a light source on the gem, it looks quite normal; simply a regular coloured opaque gem. But as soon as the light is applied, it reflects off the tips of the inclusions and the star is revealed. To maximise the star, the lapidarist will cabochon cut the gem. Prior to making their first cut, they will study the gem to predict where the asterism will take place, trying to ensure that it appears as close to the top of the dome as possible. Possibly the most famous of all Star Sapphires is the Star of India. Weighing a huge 563 carats, it is a stunning gemstone and on a recent visit to the Natural History Museum in New York, I was amazed at how long I had to queue just to walk past this star attraction. The gem was donated to the museum in 1900 by J P Morgan.

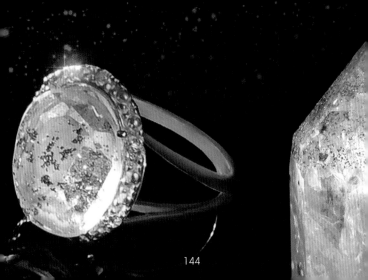

Astraeolite A gem that twinkles like the stars on a dark cloudless night.

Astaeolite is a beautiful transparent quartz that has small snowflake type of inclusions of Fool's Gold (Pyrite) magically suspended within. These are not like rutile inclusions, but are small cubic pieces of Pyrite. The miracle of nature is that these small flakes of Pyrite, rarely measuring more than one millimetre, tend to be scattered individually.

Anyone who has seen mineral specimens of Pyrite will tell you how unusual this is. The colour of the Pyrite is a gorgeous golden colour with a hue similar to that witnessed when the gem is unearthed in Spain.

When sunlight hits Astraeolite the gem visually explodes like no other gem I have seen before. Its inclusions come to life: they dance and sing. And once viewed through a microscope you become totally addicted. The gem, just like the galaxy of stars that it portrays, is nothing short of a miracle.

As the gem has so far only been discovered in one location and as of yet we are unsure of how much is hidden beneath the ground, when you see a piece you like, my advice is to grab it!

Australia Although a recently new country in terms of inhabitants, some of the oldest rocks on the planet have been discovered in Australia. This includes a Zircon discovered at Jackson Hills in Western Australia, which has been scientifically dated to have formed 4.4 billion years ago, right near the time the Earth itself was being formed.

In July 1994, the Opal was declared Australia's National Gemstone. Not surprising when you realise that the country supplies more than 90% of the world's gem-quality Opals. Mining for Opals isn't restricted to one area either, but takes place virtually all over the country.

It is believed that Opals were first discovered in Australia in the 1840s by a German gemmologist named Professor Johannes Menge, approximately 50 miles north of the then capital of South Australia, Adelaide. In the 1870s, while samples of the gem had been sent to the UK for evaluation, the first registered mining leases were being signed in the town of Quilpie (later famous for the 'Pride of the Hills' Opal mine).

Around 1900 Black Opals were discovered by children playing outdoors at Lightning Ridge. Mining in the region at the famous "Shallow Nobby's Mine" started in 1903 after a miner by the name of Charlie Nettleton walked

400 miles to set up his operation. The mine is still in operation today.

In 1915, teenager Willie Hutchinson discovered an Opal in South Australia, while panning for gold with his father, Jim Hutchison. This crucial find led to the establishment of the world's largest Opal mine named "Coober Pedy" - which, believe it or not, originates from aboriginal dialect meaning "white man in a hole".

Today it's a lot more than just a 'white man in a hole', as the town, with over 3,500 people and 45 different nationalities, is based both above and below ground. In its underground Opal mines one can find: a museum, houses, churches, gift shops and even a hotel. As far as mines go, Coober Pedy really is a rare place!

Today, for the first time in its history, Australia has now got some serious competition for its national treasure, as a recent discovery of opal in Ethiopia has uncovered a quality of gemstone that is very similar in look and appearance and one gem expert has claimed it to be "equal to if not better than Australian Opal".

Australia is the only country where Mookite is found, in Mooka Creek in Western Australia. Emerald, Agate,

Jade, Zircon and Chrysoprase are also discovered in smaller quantities.

The Argyle Diamond mine in the region of Kimberley is said to now be the biggest single producer of Diamonds in the world. As well as being the world's largest Diamond mine, "the Argyle Diamond Mine produces virtually the entire supply of the world's Pink Diamonds". They also claim to extract approximately 20 million carats of Diamonds per year.

When the mine first opened in 1985, most of the workforce was flown to the mine on a weekly basis from Perth. Over time, as the mine became established, the local towns have become more populated and now most workers have relocated. What is also quite unusual about Argyle is that it is one of the few Diamond deposits that is not hosted in kimberlite.

Australia is also one of the largest blue Sapphire suppliers in the world. Unfortunately as supply of the gem has started to dry up in Burma and Thailand, many cutting houses in Thailand have incorrectly labelled their gems as originating from their own country, in an attempt to play down the rising success of the Australian Sapphire. There are now three main deposits: two in Queensland and one in New South Wales.

150

Aventurescence If a gem's surface appearance looks metallic or as if it is painted with glitter, it is said to display aventurescence.

This optical effect happens within certain gems which feature a large amount of small disk or plate like inclusions of a mineral with a highly reflective surface (usually haematite, Pyrite or goethite). These inclusions act like tiny mirrors and produce one of nature's most fascinating optical effects.

In the mid-18th century, an Italian glass blower was said to have accidentally knocked a jar of copper filings into the molten glass he was using to create vases, and to his surprise the result was a beautiful glass featuring a metallic sparkle. The technique became widely adopted across Europe where it was used to make both jewellery and ornaments. The glass became known as "ventura", which was derived from the Italian word meaning "by chance". During the following century, a Green Quartz was discovered in Brazil which naturally produced a similar appearance to the Italian glass and was therefore named Aventurine. In addition to Aventurine, only a handful of other gems have been discovered that demonstrate this stunning lively effect, such as Moonstone, Sunstone and Labradorite.

Aventurine is a member of the Chalcedony Quartz family and is easily identified by its translucent yet sparkling appearance.

The appearance of Aventurine is so striking that its name is also used as a gemstone adjective when describing other gems with a similar sparkling optical effect: "Aventurescence".

Aventurine gets its name from the Italian word "per avventura" - which means "by chance". It is believed that in the 18th century, Venetian glass makers accidentally mixed in copper filings while producing their work and the result was a glass that sparkled.

Although green is the predominant colour for this gem, it can also be found in blue, yellow, reddish brown, greenish brown, orange and a most striking pale silvery colour.

Green Aventurine is associated with luck, chance and opportunity and is also believed to increase perception and develop creative insight.

Some highly superstitious people never buy a lottery ticket without their lucky Aventurine in their left pocket (the left pocket is chosen because both luck and left start with "L"). Aventurine is also said to increase your libido and with Tourmaline is the anniversary

153

gemstone for the 8th year of marriage.

Blue Aventurine is said to be a powerful healer that increases positivity and builds inner strength and self discipline. Several people have written that they have felt powerful and assured when wearing Blue Aventurine. If you're a non-believer in myths and legends, Aventurine remains a truly beautiful coloured gem, whose lively sparkling mica flecks will have you spellbound,("mica" is thought to come from the Latin word "mica" meaning "a crumb", most likely derived from "micare", which means "to glitter").

Aventurine has been set in jewellery for many centuries and as it is typically found in larger sizes than many other gems, has also been used to create vases, bowls and even smoking pipes. Aventurine can be found in Brazil, India, China, Japan, the Ural Mountains in Russia, Tanzania, and the USA.

Axinite 'Rare', 'stunningly beautiful' and 'a real collector's gemstone', are the first things that pop into my head when I am asked about Axinite.

There are two principle sources of this highly collectable gemstone: one in the Baltistan Valley in Northern Pakistan; and one very near to K2 (the second largest mountain in the world).

Due to the difficult weather and terrain in the region, it is only possible to operate these Axinite mines for a couple of months every year. The first parcel is from a well established mine that has been producing Axinte for around 15 years.

Its colour is a breathtaking dark brown with areas of lilac when viewed from different angles: this material does have inclusions, but this allows the gem to change colour to an almost deep reddish, purple colour. The second parcel is from a fairly new mine: it is a slightly lighter brown with amazing transparency. This parcel was very difficult to get hold of as it is mined in the tribal areas along the undefined border between Afghanistan and Pakistan and my friend Shawn went to great lengths and faced real dangers in order to obtain it for me.

Discovered at the end of the 1700s, Axinite receives its name from the fact that its unusual spatula-shaped crystals are often shaped like an axe!

Aztecs On arriving in America in the late 1400s, Spanish adventurers found two well-developed civilisations in the mid to southern regions of the country: the Incas in Peru and the often dangerous Aztec warriors of Mexico.

The reason we mention this in a gem and jewellery book, is that they were both deeply religious cultures and many of the beliefs and stories relating to the healing properties of gems originate from these civilisations.

Another reason for discussing the Aztecs is that their influence over jewellery design can still be seen in many pieces today. So fanatical were they with jewellery and gemstones that many neighbouring countries constantly worried about the threat of attack from Aztecs in search of new minerals. Not only did they craft jewellery for personal adornment and as display of authority: many would make an offering of their jewellery to their gods.

They were not just religious people, they also believed in the power of symbols and many pieces of Aztec jewellery, especially pendants and necklaces, have been unearthed where the design centres on a symbol of one kind or another.

Turquoise was incredibly popular with the Aztecs as well as several other precious stones such as Amethyst, Opals and Moonstone. Unfortunately very few gold pieces of Aztec jewellery have been preserved as much of it was melted down during the Spanish Conquest.

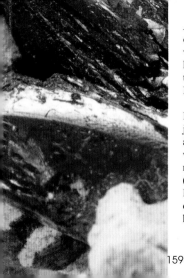

Azurite is an intensely deep-blue copper mineral, which is produced by weathered copper ore deposits. It is also known as Chessylite after the name of the mine in which it was found in Lyon, France.

Historically, the gem has been set into jewellery as well as being used in Japan as a blue pigment in paintings. Azurite was also mentioned by its previous name "Kuanos" by Pliny the Elder (author and philosopher 23– 79AD). Its vivid blue colour tends to diminish over time, especially when exposed to heat and light.

One of the most famous specimens of Azurite is known as the "Newmont Azurite". Originally discovered in Namibia in 1952, the gem was unusual for this variety in that it was over eight inches long. The miner who discovered it allegedly smuggled the gem out of the mine and sold it to pay off his tab at his local tavern.

We are unsure whether Azurite's name is derived from the Persian word "lazhward" or from the Arabic word "azul"; however both mean blue and this gemstone is instantly recognisable by its striking loud colour. As it is a fairly soft gemstone and one that is difficult to cut in larger sizes, it tends to be more of a collectable gemstone than one that can be worn.